This se
bel

....

Eny wun what looks in this diary without permishun is a Sneeky meen pig and will be sent to prissen.

The "William" Books by Richmal Crompton

1. Just—William
2. More William
3. William Again
4. William—The Fourth
5. Still—William
6. William—The Conqueror
7. William—The Outlaw
8. William—In Trouble
9. William—The Good
10. William
11. William—The Bad
12. William's Happy Days
13. William's Crowded Hours
14. William—The Pirate
15. William—The Rebel
16. William—The Gangster
17. William—The Detective
18. Sweet William
19. William—The Showman
20. William—The Dictator
21. William and Air Raid Precautions
22. William and the Evacuees
23. William Does His Bit
24. William Carries On
25. William and the Brains Trust
26. Just William's Luck
27. William—The Bold
28. William and the Tramp
29. William and the Moon Rocket
30. William and the Space Animal
31. William's Television Show
32. William—The Explorer
33. William's Treasure Trove
34. William and the Witch
35. William and the Pop Singers
36. William and the Masked Ranger
37. William the Superman
38. William the Lawless

Just—William a facsimile of the first (1922) edition

The William Companion by Mary Cadogan

The Woman Behind William: a life of Richmal Crompton by Mary Cadogan

Just William's World—a pictorial map by Gillian Clements and Kenneth Waller

School is a Waste of Time! by William Brown (and Richmal Crompton)

William the Immortal—an Illustrated Bibliography by David Schutte
(available only from David Schutte, Myrtle Cottage, Stedham GU29 0NQ)

THE WILLIAM DIARY 1995

with quotations from the William stories
by
RICHMAL CROMPTON

and pictures by
THOMAS HENRY

Selected by
DAVID SCHUTTE

MACMILLAN

First published 1994 by Pan Macmillan Children's Books
A division of Pan Macmillan Publishers Limited
Cavaye Place London SW10 9PG
and Basingstoke

Associated companies throughout the world

All the "William" books are published by Macmillan Children's Books.

ISBN 0 333 60819 4

1 3 5 7 9 8 6 4 2

A CIP catalogue record for this book is available from
the British Library

Phototypeset by CentraCet Limited, Cambridge
Printed by Cox & Wyman

ABOUT RICHMAL CROMPTON AND THOMAS HENRY

Just William, the well-meaning, irrepressible and resourceful eleven-year-old, has been with us for over seventy years, having made his first appearance in magazines as early as 1919. The stories were collected together in the first William books, *Just–William* and *More William*, in 1922. The books were an instant success. Another thirty-six followed, and they have remained a favourite with generations of children and adults ever since.

Richmal Crompton Lamburn, his creator, was born in Bury in Lancashire on 15 November 1890, the daughter of a clergyman. She studied Latin and Greek, and became a classics mistress at St Elphin's School, Derbyshire, and later at Bromley High School in Kent. She dropped her surname for writing, as she wished to hide her spare-time activities from the school authorities. An attack of polio in 1923 left her lame in one leg, and she decided to give up teaching to concentrate on her writing, which had already proved highly successful. The rest is history. She produced a total of thirty-eight William books, as well as William scripts for radio in the

1940s, and a similar number of adult novels. She died on 11 January 1969, and the last William book *William the Lawless* was published posthumously in 1970.

Thomas Henry Fisher, the man who illustrated the William stories for forty-five years, was born in Eastwood in Nottinghamshire on 30 June 1879. His first cartoon was published in 1904, and he soon became a regular contributor to famous magazines of the time such as *Punch*, *Boy's Own Paper*, *The Captain* and *Strand Magazine*. He found his perfect subject when he was asked to illustrate the William stories in 1919. In addition to the pictures and dustwrappers for the original books, he also drew scores of "William" cartoons for a periodical called the *Happy Mag*, over fifty of them in full colour. He also created a William cartoon strip for *Woman's Own*, which appeared every week from 1947 to 1962. He met Richmal Crompton only once, at a Nottingham book fair in 1958, and died on 15 October 1962 when he was half way through the illustrations for the thirty-fourth William book, *William and the Witch*.

D.S.

William invites you!

You can join the Outlaws Club!

You will receive
✱ a special Outlaws wallet containing
the new Outlaws badge
the club rules and membership card
a pad for secret messages
a club pencil
and
a letter from William giving you the secret password

To join the club send a letter with your name and address, written in block capitals, telling us you want to join the Outlaws and £2.50

The Outlaws Club
Children's Marketing Department
18–21 Cavaye Place
London SW10 9PG

You must live in the United Kingdom or the Republic of Ireland in order to join.

William says:
"I know pers'nally that the week after Christmas is a very bad time to ask anyone anything because it is so difficult to find anyone who is in a good temper. Fathers are always brooding on how much more it all cost than they had hoped it would—and that makes them almost inhuman so that at any little sound or a bit of holly on their chairs or a simple question from poor children who are merely trying to gain knowledge, they become quite frenzied."

26 ***Monday***

27 ***Tuesday***

28 ***Wednesday***

29 ***Thursday***

30 ***Friday***

31 ***Saturday***

1 ***Sunday***

How many William stories?

If you make a New Year's Resolution to read a different William story every day, starting on 1st January, they will last you up to and including Christmas Eve. That will leave you exactly a week, starting on Christmas Day, to read the only full-length book, *Just William's Luck*.

WILLIAM'S BAD RESOLUTION

"I'm sick of this New Year business," said William gloomily. "I don't get anything out of it. Jus' rotten ole good res'lutions an' everyone goin' on at you worse than what they did before."

"I know," said Ginger, "an' they won't even let you have anythin' int'restin' for a good res'lution. Jus' dull things like bein' obedient an' quiet an' clean an' suchlike. Once I tried havin' one to be an adventurer same as you read about in books, but they made such an awful fuss I had to stop."

"Pity *they* don't ever make one to be a bit kinder," put in Douglas bitterly.

The post-Christmas reaction had set in. After the excitement of presents, parties and unlimited food, life seemed to stretch before them—an unending expanse of dullness—and the suggestion of good resolutions made by their parents with tactless references to past misdeeds added insult to injury.

"I can't remember a single good res'lution I've ever made," said William, "that's turned out right. They've all got me into worse rows than if I'd not made 'em. I've a good mind to try a bad one for a change." His look of boredom vanished, and he brightened visibly. "Yes, that's a jolly good idea. I'll have a bad res'lution. It couldn't come off worse than some of my good ones have, anyway."

They looked at him with interest.

"D'you mean bein' disobedient or noisy or dirty or somethin' like that?" said Henry.

"Corks, no!" said William contemptuously. "Nothin' as dull as that! I'll be *reely* bad. Same as people in the newspapers."

"A murderer?" said Ginger awfully.

"N-no," said William. "I don't want to be a murderer 'cause they get hung. I'd be a gambler if I knew how you did it . . . A man my father knew got put in prison for promotin' a comp'ny, but I don't know how you do that either."

"What *will* you do, then?" asked Ginger.

William considered for a moment.

"Stealin's easy enough," he said at last. "I guess I'll be a burglar."

from *William and Air Raid Precautions*

William says:
"There's hundreds an' thousands of murders what no one finds out. You see, you c'n only find out a person's died nacheral by cuttin' 'em up an' they've not got time to cut everyone up what dies. They've simply not got the time. They do it like what they do with our desks at school. They jus' open one sometimes to see if it's all right."

2 ***Monday***

3 ***Tuesday***

4 ***Wednesday***

5 ***Thursday***

6 ***Friday***

7 ***Saturday***

8 ***Sunday***

William's Family

William has an older sister, Ethel, and a brother, Robert. His father's name is John and, although his mother is usually called Mary, in one early story she is called Margaret.

William was upstairs in his bedroom, composing his first begging letter.

Dear Sir

I am a pore man out of work with eighteen children who are all very ill. My wife is very ill. I am very ill. My mother and father are very ill. If you do not send some money we shall all dye. Besides being out of work and very ill I am def and dum. All my children are def and dum. My wife is def and dum. My mother and father are def and dum. Plees send a lot of money to get us all cured. It is very expensive getting cured of being def and dum.

Yours cinserely,
William Brown

9 *Monday*

10 *Tuesday*

11 ***Wednesday***

12 ***Thursday***

13 ***Friday***

14 ***Saturday***

15 ***Sunday***

Hubert turned his small malignant eyes upon William.

"You've not got a watch," he said.

"Huh!" he said, "a lot you know about it."

"I know you've not got one."

"Oh, do you," said William sarcastically. "Well, you know a bit too much. Let me tell you my aunt gave me one for Christmas."

"Yes, and you tried to make a bomb out of it last week with some gunpowder, and a lot of things in your house got blown up, and there wasn't any of the watch left at all, and your father said you'd not to have another one till you were twenty-one even if anyone gave you one."

16 ***Monday***

17 ***Tuesday***

18 ***Wednesday***

19 ***Thursday***

20 ***Friday***

21 ***Saturday***

22 ***Sunday***

JANUARY

WILLIAM BRIGHTENS UP A FROSTY MORNING

from *The Happy Mag*, February 1927

William says:

"A sivel war means a war where they didn't fight very hard and were polite to each other. The most famous man in the sivel wars was called Nelson, and he was the man who played a joke on Queen Elizabeth.

He put his coat over a puddle so that she shouldn't know that it was a puddle, and she stepped on it and went in splash and everyone laughed. In the end he was beheaded for inventing potatoes and cigarettes. They beheaded people for anything in those days."

23 ***Monday***

24 ***Tuesday***

25 ***Wednesday***

26 ***Thursday***

27 ***Friday***

28 ***Saturday***

29 ***Sunday***

What the Outlaws Drink

Their favourite is liquorice water, made by shaking up small pieces of liquorice in a bottle of water. Try it and see what it tastes like!

"Makes me feel *mad*," said William. "Miners havin' Trades Unions an' Strikes an' things to stop 'em doin' too *much* work an' *us* havin' to go on an' on an' *on* at school till we're wore out. You'd think Parliament'd stop it. People go on writin' in the papers about people needin' fresh air an' then 'stead of lettin' people *have* fresh air they shut 'em up in schools all day, mornin' *an'* afternoon, till—till they're all wore out."

30 ***Monday***

31 ***Tuesday***

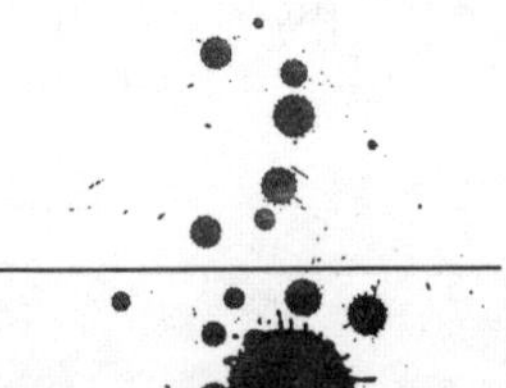

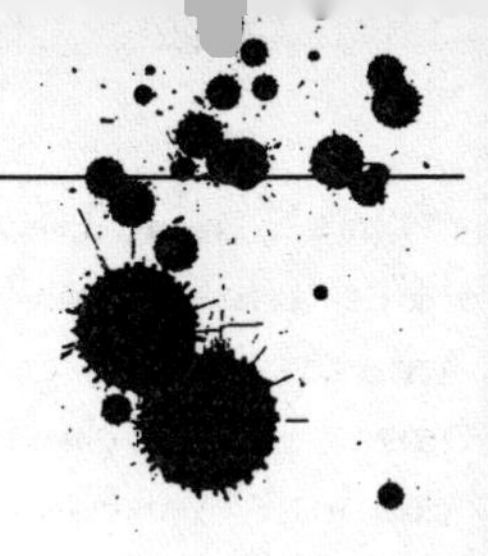

1 *Wednesday*

2 *Thursday*

3 *Friday*

4 *Saturday*

5 *Sunday*

"They're dead boys," one of the spectators was saying in low fearful tones. "I know they're dead boys. My brother told me. The shop-man goes out after dark catchin' 'em. Then when he's killed 'em he dressed 'em up an' puts 'em in his shop window. If you was to come past his shop after dark he'd get you. My brother said so. My brother once met him after dark carryin' a sack over his shoulder . . ."

6 *Monday*

7 *Tuesday*

8 ***Wednesday***

---

9 ***Thursday***

---

10 ***Friday***

---

11 ***Saturday***

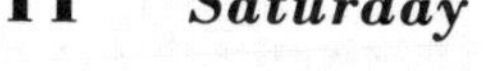

---

12 ***Sunday***

WILLIAM AND SAINT VALENTINE

Ethel and the young man began to talk together again. They had evidently decided to ignore William's presence. William listened with rapt attention. He wanted to know what you said and the sort of voice you said it in.

"St Valentine's Day next week," said Laurence soulfully.

"Oh, no one takes any notice of that nowadays," said Ethel.

"I'm going to," said Laurence. "I think it's a beautiful idea. Its meaning, you know . . . true love . . . If I send you a Valentine, will you accept it?"

"That depends on the Valentine," said Ethel with a smile.

"It's the thought that's behind it that's the vital thing," said Laurence soulfully. "It's that that matters. Ethel . . . you're in all my waking dreams."

"I'm sure I'm not," said Ethel.

"You are . . . Has anyone ever told you before that you're a perfect Botticelli?"

"Heaps of people," said Ethel calmly.

"I was thinking about love last night," said Laurence. "Love at first sight. That's the only sort of love . . . When first I saw you my heart leapt at the sight of you." Laurence was a great reader of romances. "I think that we're predestined for each other. We must have known each other in former existences. We——"

"Do speak up," said William irritably. "You're speaking so low that I can't hear what you're saying."

"*What!*"

The young man turned a flaming face of fury on to him. William returned his gaze quite unabashed.

"I don' mean I want you to *shout*," said William, "but just speak so's I can hear."

The young man turned to Ethel.

"Can you get a wrap and come into the garden?" he said.

"Yes . . . I've got one in the hall," said Ethel, rising.

William fetched his coat and patiently accompanied them round the garden.

from *Still—William*

"What I think's so awful," said William, seated firmly on one of his favourite hobby-horses, "is that I've lived all these years and not *done* anything yet."

"You've done quite enough," said his mother. "You've broken every window in this house at one time or another, you've made the geyser explode twice, you've *ruined* the parquet by sliding on it, and you've got tar all over the hall carpet."

"Well, I can't help them putting tar on the roads, can I?" said William, stung by the injustice of this accusation. "I've got to walk somewhere, haven't I? I can't fly, can I? It's not fair to blame *me* because people put tar on the roads. Besides, I didn't mean that sort of thing, anyway. I meant the sort of thing that makes you famous. The sort of thing people put up statues to you for. I meant, it's awful to think of me living all these years an' not done anythin' yet to make the world ring with my name."

13 *Monday*

14 *Tuesday*

15 ***Wednesday***

16 ***Thursday***

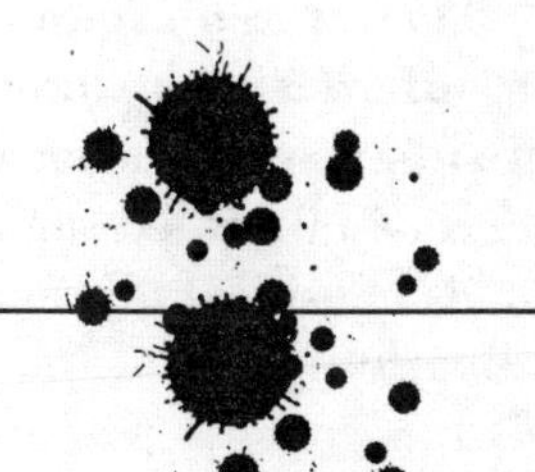

17 ***Friday***

18 ***Saturday***

19 ***Sunday***

"William said he'd discovered gas, said he'd discovered electricity, said he'd climbed Mount Everest, and discovered the North Pole. Said he could make himself invisible."

Suddenly William's voice came, startling them into silence.

"Well, I've done it. All but my shoes. I found I couldn't do leather. I could do everything but leather."

They stared around them, open-mouthed. Then with a cry of excitement someone pointed to William's shoes that stood at a convincing angle on the grass.

"I say," gasped someone. "Are you there, William?"

"Course I am," replied William's voice. "I'm invisible all right."

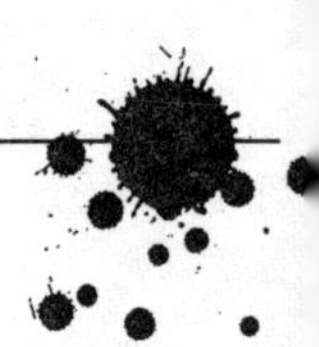

20 *Monday*

21 *Tuesday*

FEBRUARY

22 *Wednesday*

23 *Thursday*

24 *Friday*

25 *Saturday*

26 *Sunday*

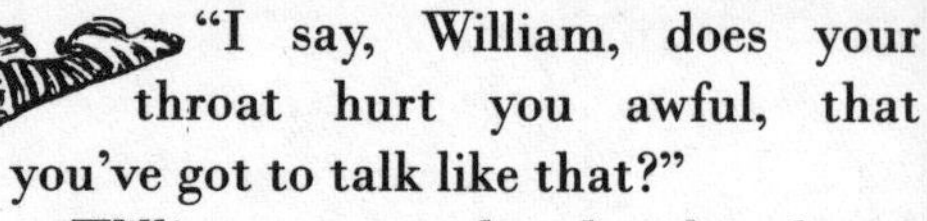

"I say, William, does your throat hurt you awful, that you've got to talk like that?"

William put one hand to his throat and frowned.

"A bit," he confessed lightly.

She started up and stared at him with big blue eyes.

"Oh, William! Is it—is it your—lungs? I've got an aunt that's got lungs and she coughs and coughs," William coughed hastily, "and it hurts her and makes her awful bad. Oh, William, I do *hope* you've got no lungs."

Her tender, anxious little face was upturned to him. "I guess I have got lungs," he said, "but I don't make a fuss about 'em."

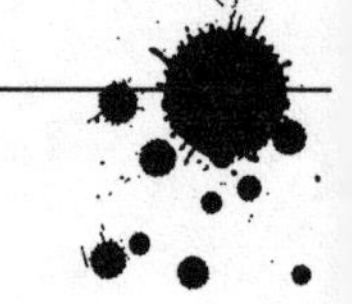

27 ***Monday***

28 ***Tuesday***

1 *Wednesday*

2 *Thursday*

3 *Friday*

4 *Saturday*

5 *Sunday*

WILLIAM THE DICTATOR—WOULD MAKE THE WORLD BETTER AND BRIGHTER

from *The Happy Mag*, February 1934

William paused in the hall in order to place his cap on the antlered head of a deer that hung on the wall next the hat-stand. It was William's custom to put his cap there, trying different angles to obtain different effects. And as Emily's mood could be gauged from her handling of the dinner gong, so could Mr Brown's from his reaction to his younger son's cap on the deer's head. There were days when he smiled at it indulgently, there were days when he altered it slightly in order to enhance the effect that William had obviously been aiming at, there were days when he snatched it up with an explosive sound of wrath and flung it on to one of the hat-stand hooks.

To-day, William had not time to do more than draw the peak of his cap down over the bleary glass eyes, imparting a slightly sinister look to the vapid countenance.

6 *Monday*

7 *Tuesday*

8 ***Wednesday***

9 ***Thursday***

10 ***Friday***

11 ***Saturday***

12 ***Sunday***

William says:
"It always seems extraordinary to me the way ink spreads upwards from your pen to your fingers and hands, even, sometimes, right to your elbows."

13 *Monday*

14 *Tuesday*

15 *Wednesday*

16 ***Thursday***

17 ***Friday***

18 ***Saturday***

19 ***Sunday***

Did you know?

Ginger's older brother is called Hector. Richmal Crompton sometimes refers to Ginger's surname as Flowerdew and sometimes as Merridew.

"I'm a jolly good speller," said William. "Sometimes I spell a bit diff'rent from other people but I b'lieve in—in"—he searched for the word in his mind then finally brought out—"this deformed spellin' that Parliament's goin' to make a lor of."

20 *Monday*

21 *Tuesday*

22 *Wednesday*

23 *Thursday*

24 *Friday*

25 *Saturday*

26 *Sunday*

APRIL FOOL'S DAY

"I wish we could find someone that had forgotten it was April Fool's Day," said Henry.

"Tell you what I'd like to do," said William dreamily. "I'd like to make someone really important, like the King or Parliament, an April Fool."

"You couldn't."

"Yes, I could. I could eas'ly. I could ring them up and say that an enemy had landed and they'd call out the army and march down to the coast and find no one there. I bet they'd be April Fools all right."

"You don't know their telephone number."

"No, but I could look them up in the book, couldn't I, silly?"

"You'd prob'ly get executed."

"Yes, I know. That's why I'm not goin' to do it. Not to the King and Parliament anyway. But I'd like to make someone important an April Fool, but not as important as the King or Parliament. Let's think who's the most important person living here."

"The Vicar," suggested Ginger.

"The doctor," suggested Douglas.

"Yes, I think the doctor," said William. "He'd be easier to make one, anyway . . . I know! I've thought of something to bring them *both* in."

Followed by his Outlaws, William made his way up to the doctor's front door, knocked at it smartly, and informed the maid who opened it that the Vicar was dying and would the doctor please go to him at once. For answer he received a box on the ear that nearly made him lose his balance. He rejoined his friends, rubbing his boxed ear tenderly and filled with righteous indignation.

"S'pose it was true, an' they'd let the poor Vicar die. Well, I think she's the same as a murderer, that woman is. I've a good mind to go an' *tell* the Vicar that she's as good as murdered him . . ."

from *William—The Rebel*

William says:

"When I'm a millionaire, I'm goin' to break ten windows every day. I'm goin' to keep a window mender in my house all the time mendin' the windows ready for me to break 'em again. An' I'm not goin' to have any flowers or paths in the garden. I'm jus' goin' to let it go wild with long grass an' trees. An' I'm goin' to buy a lot of wild animals from the Zoo to live in it—elephants an' lions an' tigers an' giraffes an' things like that. All livin' wild in the garden—but we'll tame them so's they'll be tame with us but wild with everyone else. I'm not goin' to have any flowers in the garden. I never see any sense in flowers."

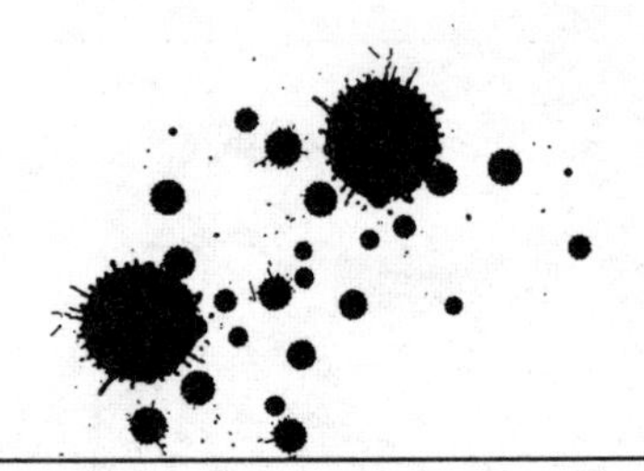

27 ***Monday***

28 ***Tuesday***

29 *Wednesday*

30 *Thursday*

31 *Friday*

1 *Saturday*

2 *Sunday*

William says:
"It would of course be nice to be famous and one can always become famous by discovering something like the man what became famous by discovering that apples fall to the ground. It's always been a mystery to me why people make such a fuss about him because you'd have thought that if they'd used their eyes they'd have seen for themselves that apples fall to the ground."

3 *Monday*

4 *Tuesday*

5 ***Wednesday***

6 ***Thursday***

7 ***Friday***

8 ***Saturday***

9 ***Sunday***

William says:
"Meanness, that's what it is. Meanness. Anythin' to keep our pocket-money themselves 'stead of givin' it to us. Seems to me they go about makin' things easy to break so's they c'n have an excuse for keeping it themselves instead of givin' it us. *Meanness*. That's what it is."

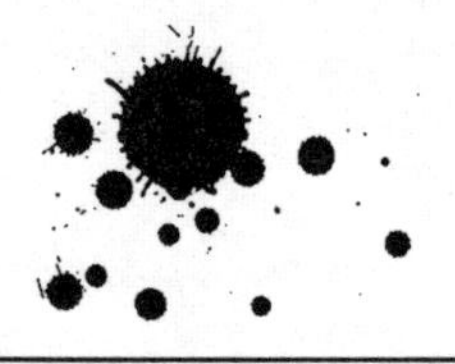

10 ***Monday***

11 ***Tuesday***

12 ***Wednesday***

13 ***Thursday***

14 ***Friday***

15 ***Saturday***

16 ***Sunday***

Did you know?

Violet Elizabeth Bott first appeared in a story called "The Sweet Little Girl in White" (*Still—William*). She is in thirty-two stories altogether.

"Yes," said William, "but you don't know what *kind* of a penknife my Uncle Charles is givin' me. I've got three penknives, an' one's almost as big as a nornery knife, an' got four blades *an'* a thing for taking stones out of horses' hoofs *an'* some things what I haven't found out what they're meant for yet, an' this what he's given me is a baby penknife—it's only got one blade, an' I heard him tellin' mother that I couldn't do any harm with it. Fancy"—his voice quivered with indignation—"*fancy* anyone givin' you a penknife what you can't do any harm with."

17 *Monday*

18 *Tuesday*

19 ***Wednesday***

20 ***Thursday***

21 ***Friday***

22 ***Saturday***

23 ***Sunday***

WILLIAM'S HIKING HOLIDAY

from *The Happy Mag*, September 1936

William says:
"If I were the king I'd make everyone stop bein' civilized an' start bein' savages again an' I bet we'd all be a jolly sight happier."

24 *Monday*

25 *Tuesday*

APRIL

26 ***Wednesday***

27 ***Thursday***

28 ***Friday***

29 ***Saturday***

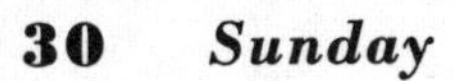

30 ***Sunday***

William's pocket money was mortgaged for a month to come in order to pay for the crockery he had broken while training to be a juggler.

"Well, they've all gotter learn, haven't they?" he had protested passionately, when sentence was passed on him. "Gosh! D'you think jugglers can throw up plates like that without practisin'? D'you think they're *born* throwin' up plates like that? They've gotter break a few plates an' things practisin'. Stands to reason . . . Well, how'm I goin' to earn my livin' bein' a juggler when I'm grown up if you won't let me practise? Anyone'd think you didn't *want* me to earn my livin' when I'm grown up. It's goin' to be jolly expensive to you keepin' me all my life, just 'cause you won't ever let me start practisin' to earn my livin' jugglin' . . ."

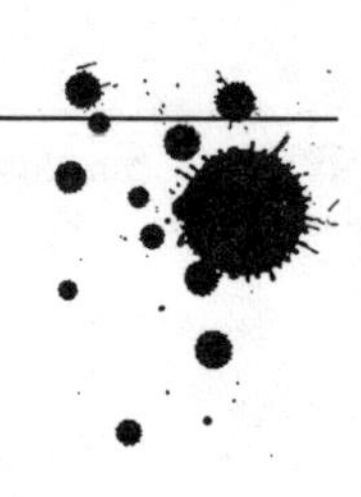

1 *Monday*

2 *Tuesday*

3 *Wednesday*

4 *Thursday*

5 *Friday*

6 *Saturday*

7 *Sunday*

In a muffled voice William explained that the whole of his face except his eyes and mouth was blown away. The crowd, clustered around him in the cloakroom, hung breathless upon his words. Suggestions and queries were hurled at him from all sides.

"What you're goin' to do? I'd wear a mask. I'd get a funny one that'd make people laugh."

"Don't see how your eyes stick in if there's nothin' for 'em to stick to," said another.

"I bet you twopence they fall out when he starts to run," offered a youthful sportsman.

8 ***Monday***

9 ***Tuesday***

10 ***Wednesday***

11 ***Thursday***

12 ***Friday***

13 ***Saturday***

14 ***Sunday***

"What's a stone's throw?" said Ginger.

"What d'you mean, what's a stone's throw?" said William.

"Well, my aunt's goin' to live in a new house an' the estate agent said it was a stone's throw from the shops."

William picked up a stone.

"I'll show you what a stone's throw is," he said.

He meant to throw the stone along the road but Jumble, taking the action as an invitation to a game, leapt up exuberantly and flung him off his balance.

The stone soared over the hedge into the garden they were passing.

There came the sinister sound of breaking glass.

"Gosh!" said William in horror.

15 ***Monday***

16 ***Tuesday***

17 ***Wednesday***

18 ***Thursday***

19 ***Friday***

20 ***Saturday***

21 ***Sunday***

William on picnics:

"You'd never think that sardines and ginger beer and cream and hawthorn berries all squashed up together would taste nice, would you? But it does. As long as you don't eat a lot of it. When you've eaten a lot of it it starts tasting different."

22 ***Monday***

23 ***Tuesday***

24 ***Wednesday***

25 ***Thursday***

26 ***Friday***

27 ***Saturday***

28 ***Sunday***

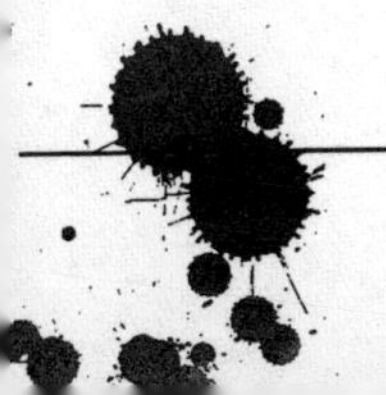

WILLIAM'S DAY OFF

William is pretending to be a boy from the slums who has never seen the countryside before.

"Grass, mum?" William said in his deep, throaty voice. "What's grass?"

Miss Milton was taken aback for a moment. Surely even slum children knew what grass was. But evidently they didn't, so she hastened to explain.

"That's grass," she said, pointing to her sister's sparse little lawn. "It's—well, it's just grass," she ended lamely.

William began to feel that a certain amount of enjoyment might, after all, be extracted from the situation.

He pointed over the hedge to a cow that was pleasantly ruminating in the next field.

"What's that?" he gruffed.

"That's a cow."

"What's a cow?"

Miss Milton sighed. But, of course, it was quite natural that a slum child should never have seen a cow.

"It's—just a cow, dear," she said. "A cow is—well, it's a cow."

Miss Milton's cat sauntered out of the kitchen door and eyed William sardonically.

"What's that?" he said, pointing at it.

"A cat, of course," said Miss Milton rather sharply. "Surely you've seen cats at home."

William realised that he was rather overdoing his town-bred ignorance.

"It's bigger than town cats," he said hastily.

"I suppose it is," said Miss Milton, appeased.

The cat, who had recognised William, winked at him and went indoors again.

Miss Milton told him the names of the various flowers as they went round the garden.

"That's a viola, dear, and that's a campanula, and that's an antirrhinum . . ."

William thought wistfully of Marleigh caves and wished that he was there with the others.

from *William and Air Raid Precautions*

William says:

"Earwigs make nice pets. They say that if they ever manage to get into a person's ear—which they're always tryin' to—they work their way right into your brain.

A boy once told me that he'd got an aunt that that happened to and they had to put lettuces and things like that at her other ear to get it to come out again that way."

29 *Monday*

30 *Tuesday*

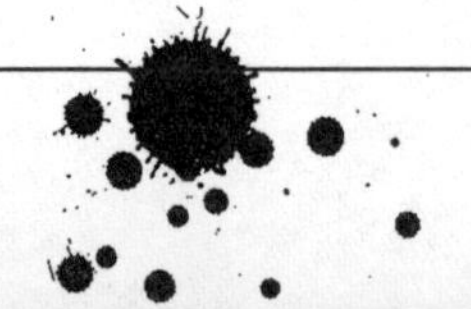

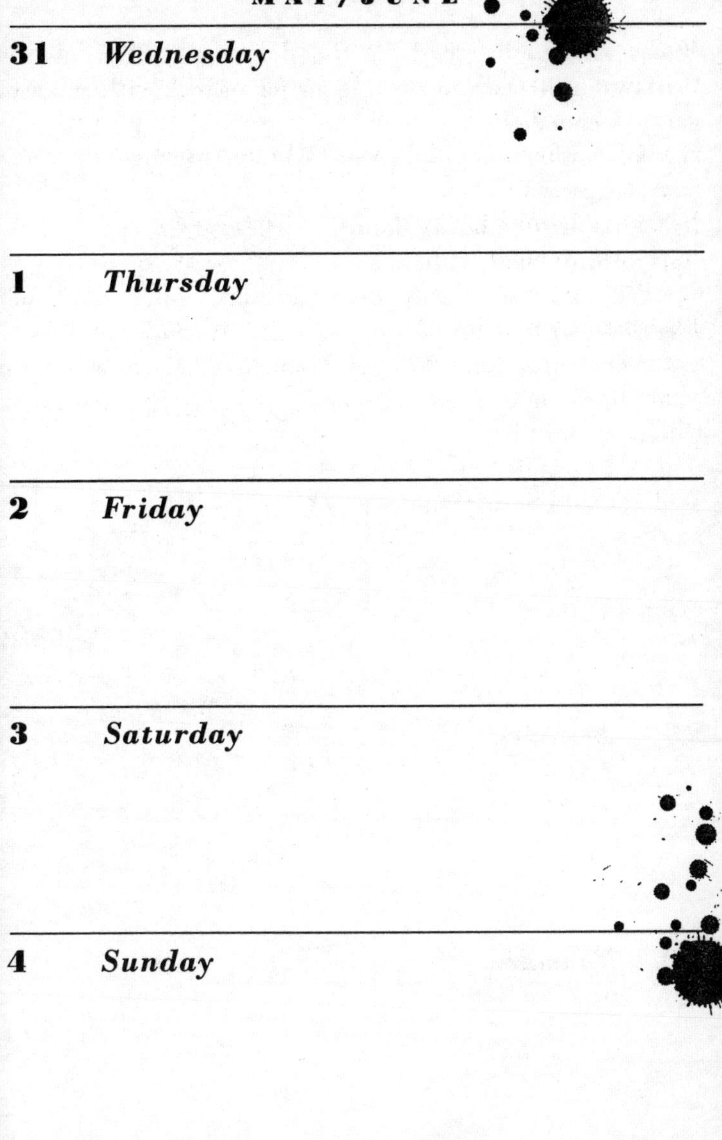

31 ***Wednesday***

1 ***Thursday***

2 ***Friday***

3 ***Saturday***

4 ***Sunday***

Violet Elizabeth stood in the doorway, gazing at the Outlaws in silence and sucking a stick of rock with an air of gentle melancholy.

"We don't want you," said William brusquely. "We're busy. Go away."

"What are you buthy doin'?" she demanded.

"Nothin'," said William succinctly.

"You can't be buthy doin' nothin'," objected Violet Elizabeth with an air of deep wisdom. "It ithn't pothible."

"Yeth, it ith," said William, mimicking her voice and lisp in a forlorn hope of annoying her. But Violet Elizabeth took the rock out of her mouth and smiled at William with devastating sweetness.

"You are *funny*, William," she said.

5 *Monday*

6 *Tuesday*

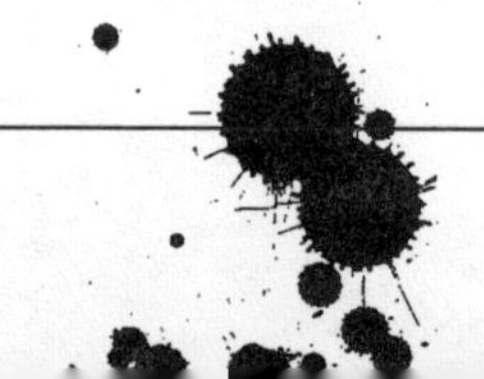

7 *Wednesday*

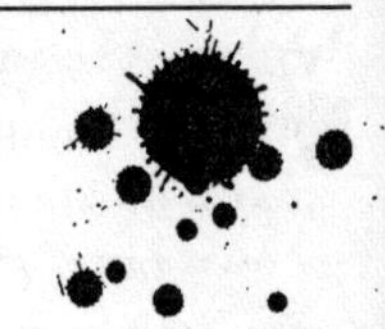

8 *Thursday*

9 *Friday*

10 *Saturday*

11 *Sunday*

Bunker, the old black cat, had been an inhabitant of William's home ever since he could remember.

William treated all cats with supreme contempt. Towards his own family cat he unbent occasionally so far as to throw twigs at it or experiment upon it with pots of coloured paints, but he prided himself upon despising cats, and considered that their only use in the world was to give exercise and pleasure to his beloved mongrel, Jumble.

12 ***Monday***

13 ***Tuesday***

14 ***Wednesday***

15 ***Thursday***

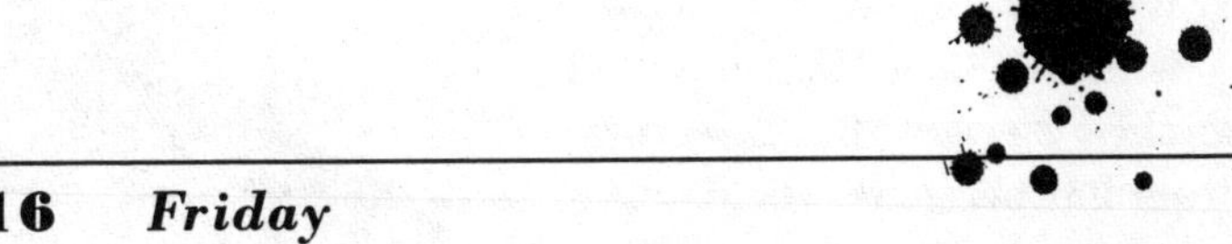

16 ***Friday***

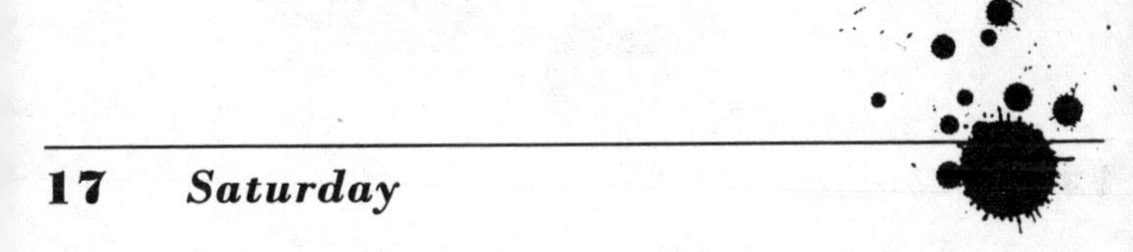

17 ***Saturday***

18 ***Sunday***

Hubert lay in bed, gazing at the clock on his mantelpiece. It seemed to have an irresistible fascination for him. He tried to close his eyes and go to sleep but he couldn't. He kept opening them to look at the clock. Ten o'clock . . . five past ten . . . ten past ten . . . quarter past ten . . . twenty past ten . . . twenty-five past ten . . . half past ten . . . He had to do it. He simply couldn't help himself. He slipped out of bed, opened the window curtains and peeped out . . . And then — his blood froze, his eyes dilated with horror and his plump face turned a delicate green. For, coming in at the gate, was the scarecrow from Farmer Jenks' field.

19 ***Monday***

20 ***Tuesday***

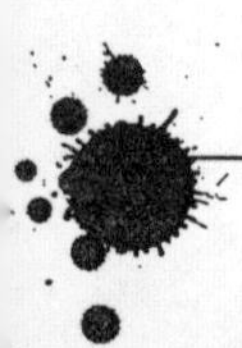

21 ***Wednesday***

22 ***Thursday***

23 ***Friday***

24 ***Saturday***

25 ***Sunday***

So annoyed was William with his family that, in order to punish them, he lost his voice. This, of course, alone, would have been a reward rather than a punishment, but he insisted on writing all he had to say (which was a lot) on a slate with a squeaky slate-pencil that went through everyone's head. They gave him paper and pencil, and he deliberately broke the point on the first word, and then returned to his squeaky slate-pencil to explain and apologise at agonising length. Finally, in despair, they sent over to the doctor for some medicine which proved so nauseous that William's voice returned.

26 *Monday*

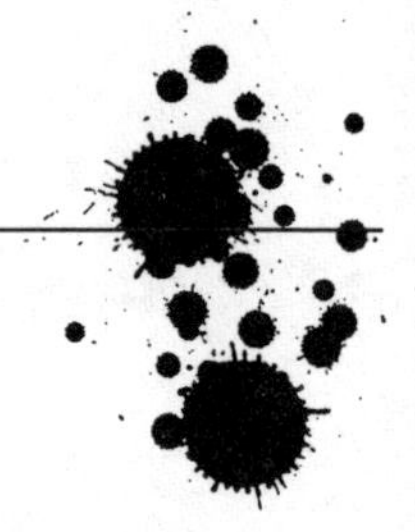

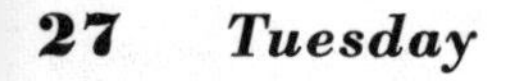

27 *Tuesday*

28 *Wednesday*

29 ***Thursday***

30 ***Friday***

1 ***Saturday***

2 ***Sunday***

Did you know?

Douglas's brother is called George. He also has a sister, but Richmal Crompton does not tell us her name.

WILLIAM AND THE SEA-SIDE SHOW

"We're not goin' to the sea-side this year," announced William.

"Nor us," said Ginger.

"Nor us," said Douglas.

"Nor us," said Henry.

"Seems silly to me," said William after a slight pause, "that the sea-side should only be at the sea. Seems to me that if only people'd take a bit of trouble they could have it anywhere."

"How could they?" challenged Ginger.

"Well, there mus' be some way," said William. "There's some way of doin' everythin' if only you can think of it. How d'you think people'd have invented electricity an' motors an' potato peelers an' things if there hadn't been?"

"But there's got to be *sea* at the sea-side," said Douglas. "You can't have sea-side anywhere but at the sea."

"Well, what's the sea but water?" replied William. "An' you can have water anywhere, can't you?"

"Yes, but——" said Douglas uncertainly.

"Rivers are water, aren't they?" went on William, pursuing his theme, "an' ponds are water. The sea's just the same as a lot of rivers an' ponds stuck together, isn't it?"

"There's salt in the sea," said Henry triumphantly.

"Well, you can put salt in a pond, can't you?" snapped William. "Don't keep makin' such silly objections. Salt's cheap enough, isn't it?"

"There's sand at the sea-side," said Ginger.

"Well, what's sand but yellow earth?" said William. "I bet it's easy enough to turn earth yellow. Come to that, there's lots of sand where they're makin' those new houses. I bet I could bring down enough to make a sea-side. They stop workin' there at five."

"But—there's piers an' promenades an' pierrots at the sea-side," said Henry.

"Well, what's piers but a bit of wood stuck out into the water? An' a promenade's only a bit of ground for walkin' about on, an' pierrots only people with their faces blacked. All you want to make a sea-side is a bit of water an' a bit of salt an' a bit of wood an' a bit of ground an' some blacking. I bet I could make one's easy's easy. We'd charge money, of course, for lettin' people come to it. I bet we'd make a jolly lot of money."

from *William—The Showman*

William says:

"If any of you are thinking of going to the British Museum I can jolly well tell you that it's not worth going to. It's full of great huge broken statues and nothing else. You'd think they'd have got someone to mend them up a bit, wouldn't you? Or else thrown them away and got some new ones. There must have been lots of jumble sales they could have sent them to since they got broke."

3 ***Monday***

4 ***Tuesday***

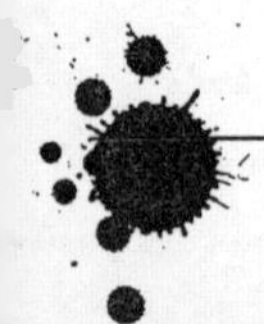

5 *Wednesday*

6 *Thursday*

7 *Friday*

8 *Saturday*

9 *Sunday*

WILLIAM'S OVER-TEN CLUB

"Well, look at him," said William, pointing to the baby and shifting his line of attack in his turn. "What's he doin' here, anyway? You can't say *he's* over ten."

The baby stared at William dispassionately for a few moments then bent his whole attention to the work of blowing bubbles with his saliva.

"He's two," chorused the meeting. "We know he's two 'cause his mother says so. An' Arabella's nine 'cause we *know* she is."

A smile of triumph curved Arabella's thin lips.

"Well, that makes us a person of eleven between us, doesn't it? so we *can* b'long. We can b'long as a person of eleven, so *there*, William Brown!"

10 ***Monday***

11 ***Tuesday***

12 *Wednesday*

13 *Thursday*

14 *Friday*

15 *Saturday*

16 *Sunday*

Violet Elizabeth's "Croth-word Puthle"

1 down—Wot you hav dropps of.
1 acros—Oppossit of cat.

"Can't you gueth it, William?" said Violet Elizabeth with triumph in her voice, "ith cough an' dog. C-O-F– Cough."

"You don't have drops of cough," said William scornfully.

"Yeth, you do, William," said Violet Elizabeth. "You have cough dropth. I've had them. I've had cough dropth, I have."

"You don't spellem like that anyway," said William.

"Well, how *do* you thpellem?" said Violet Elizabeth.

William, who was rather hazy on the point, quickly changed the subject.

"Well, what's the opposite of cat?"

"Dog, William."

"Dog isn't the opposite of cat."

"Yeth it ith, William," said Violet Elizabeth sweetly "'cauth I *know* it ith."

17 ***Monday***

18 ***Tuesday***

19 ***Wednesday***

20 ***Thursday***

21 ***Friday***

22 ***Saturday***

23 ***Sunday***

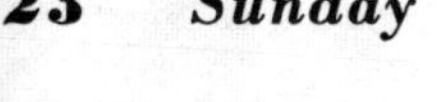

William says:

"If ever you want to go to the Zoo don't go with my aunt. She won't go into the lion place because it gives her a headache and she won't go into the bear place because she says it's dangerous and she won't go into the snake pit because she says it makes her feel faint and she won't go into the parrot place because she says they use bad language and she won't go into the fish place because you have to pay."

24 *Monday*

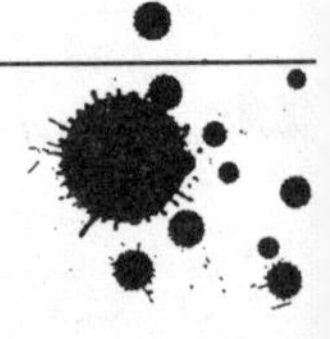

25 *Tuesday*

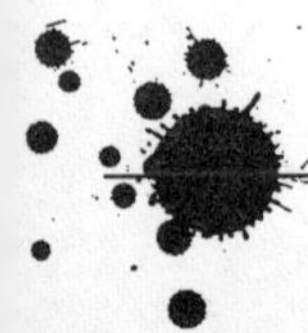

26 *Wednesday*

27 *Thursday*

28 *Friday*

29 *Saturday*

30 *Sunday*

William says:

"I think that shopkeepers ought to have a change from shopkeeping in the holidays, especially in the sweet-shops. I think that boys ought to take over the sweet-shops for them while they're having the change. I think that the sweet-shop keepers charge far too much money for their sweets. I'd sell them a good deal cheaper, and I'd eat a good deal many myself, of course, because a shopkeeper has to do that to stop them getting stale."

31 *Monday*

1 *Tuesday*

2 ***Wednesday***

3 ***Thursday***

4 ***Friday***

5 ***Saturday***

6 ***Sunday***

WILLIAM TAKES A TRIP TO THE SEASIDE—AND SPENDS A VERY BUSY DAY

AUGUST

from *The Happy Mag*, July 1934

They made their way down the lane to Miss Milton's cottage and stood at the gate for a few moments, surveying the herbaceous border.

"Yes, it's overcrowded all right," said William assuming a critical air. "It cert'ly needs a bit of thinnin' out."

They set to work on the plants with trowel, fork, secateurs, and daisy-grubber. They dug them up, they pulled them up, they tore them up, they hacked them up. There had been a heavy shower in the night. The soil was moist and the roots came away easily. They filled the trug. They filled their pockets. Mud-stained but triumphant, they returned to Wayside Cottage, leaving a trail of odds and ends of herbaceous plants along the lane to mark their progress.

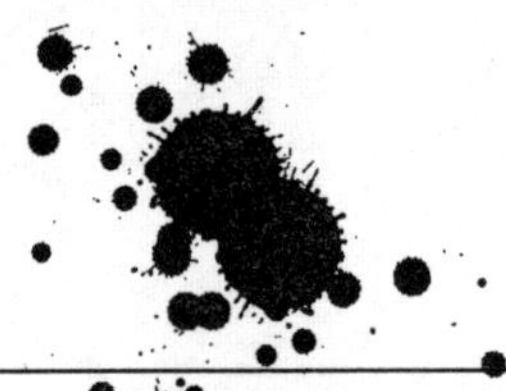

7 ***Monday***

8 ***Tuesday***

9 *Wednesday*

10 *Thursday*

11 *Friday*

12 *Saturday*

13 *Sunday*

How William Would Improve the Seaside:
There are a lot of ways in which I think that seaside places might be made nicer for people's summer holidays. To begin with I think it would be much more exciting if the piers weren't fastened to the land like they are. I think it would be very jolly to go floating with the tide and if it was windy you might get carried out to foreign places which would be very exciting. Or if it wasn't windy enough for that you might get carried round the coast to different seaside places, only that wouldn't be quite as interesting as it sounds because they're all exactly alike.

14 ***Monday***

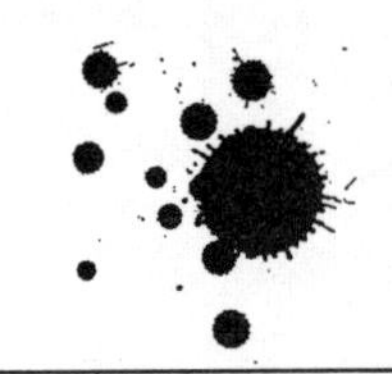

15 ***Tuesday***

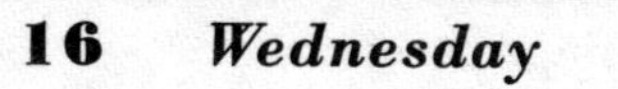

16 ***Wednesday***

17 ***Thursday***

18 ***Friday***

19 ***Saturday***

20 ***Sunday***

William read the letter with frowning concentration.

Dear William

We can't come home because we let it to Miss Evesham unfurnished and we can't get her out and Mummy and I want to come home and do you remember when we were turned out because of that bomb you got us back and *please*, William, will you get us back again because Mummy and I are both so homesick and you're so clever I know you can.

Love from Joan

He liked Joan. She was quiet and shy, and amenable and dependable, and he was a god in her eyes. The last alone would have endeared her to William, who was a god in very few people's eyes. He had never failed her yet, and to fail in this task she so disconcertingly thrust upon him might be to lose her admiration for ever.

21 ***Monday***

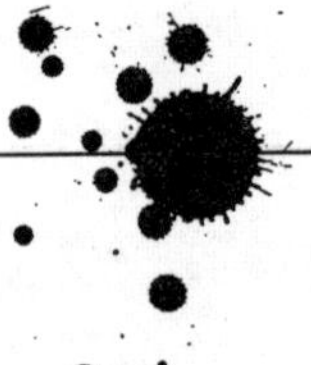

22 ***Tuesday***

23 ***Wednesday***

24 ***Thursday***

25 ***Friday***

26 ***Saturday***

27 ***Sunday***

WILLIAM AND THE EARLY ROMANS

"Pots don' hold water stuck with glue," said William scathingly. "I've tried 'em. I don't see what use findin' bits of broken pots is, anyway. I could *give* 'em lots of broken pots out of our dustbin if that's all they want. Our housemaid, she's always breakin' pots. She'd've made a fine ancient Roman, she would. Seems to me these ancient Romans wasn't much use spite o' bein' cracked up so—spendin' all their time breakin' pots."

"They *didn't*," said Henry, exasperated. "The pots only got broken with bein' buried."

"Well," said William triumphantly, "think of that—buryin' pots! 'S almost as silly as breakin' em. Think of a race of men like what the ancient Romans is supposed to have been, spendin' all their time *buryin' pots* . . . I always *knew* there was something fishy about those Romans."

28 ***Monday***

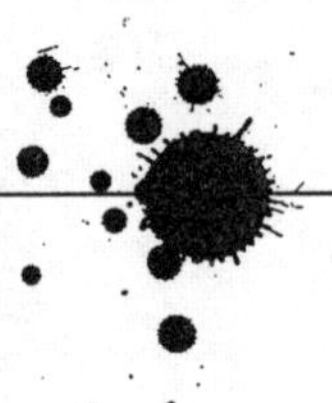

29 ***Tuesday***

30 ***Wednesday***

31 ***Thursday***

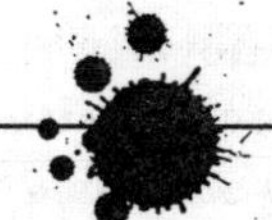

1 ***Friday***

2 ***Saturday***

3 ***Sunday***

WILLIAM AT THE GARDEN PARTY

William saw Ethel coming to fetch him to join his family for tea.

He had lost his cap, his hair stood straight on end, the rock and toffee and chocolate and ices had left visible marks of their passing in large circles round his mouth. His efforts at the coconut shy stall had sent his collar and tie round to the region of his left ear, his hands were black and sticky and his knees, where he had fallen when jumping to and fro over the fence at the back of the coconut shy stall, were covered with mud.

Ethel shuddered and winced at the sight. The thought of this object's joining the well-dressed Brown party around the dainty little table in the tea enclosure was too horrible.

"Do you want any tea, William?" she said.

"Yes," said William, his mouth full of rock.

Ethel handed him sixpence.

"I'll give you that," she said, "not to want any tea."

William pocketed it.

"Now do you want any tea?" said Ethel.

"No," said William, trying unsuccessfully to jump over the bran tub (which was left temporarily unattended) and bringing bran tub and himself to the ground. He got up, brushed off a certain amount of bran from his person and hurried away from the scene of disaster.

Reaching the shelter of a large tree, he took out Ethel's sixpence to gaze at it fondly. It did not occur to him to wonder why Ethel did not want him to want any tea. The ways of the grown-up world were so full of mystery that he never even attempted to solve them. He'd got sixpence—that was the main thing—and he could get far nicer things himself with sixpence than you ever got at any old grown-up tea. Whistling discordantly, with his hands in his pockets, he set off to buy another stick of rock, then he bought another bar of chocolate, then he had another ride on the roundabout, then he had another coconut shy.

from *William—In Trouble*

William says:
"At first sight, French seems more natural and reasonable than Latin because the French people have not all died off same as the Latin people have (and I don't wonder the Latin people have all died off, having to speak a language like that), and may possibly come to England and want to talk to us in their own language. But the weak point of all this is that the French we are taught in schools is not the language that people talk in France. I know this for a fact because once, when I had been learning French for a whole term at school, I met a French boy and the French boy and I did not understand a word each other said all the afternoon, but we got on all right. They evidently fight in France just the same way as we do over here."

4 *Monday*

5 *Tuesday*

6 ***Wednesday***

7 ***Thursday***

8 ***Friday***

9 ***Saturday***

10 ***Sunday***

William heard no sound of her approach. Suddenly a hand was laid on his shoulder from behind and looking up with a start his eyes met the eyes of the woman with the pince-nez and elaborately-dressed hair. All about him were the signs of his guilt. His jar containing his morning's "bag" stood on one side of him together with a little pile of apples gathered for refreshment in the intervals of fishing. On the other side of him lay a little heap of cores representing refreshments already taken. His pockets bulged with apples. His mouth was full of apple. He held a half-eaten apple in one hand and his rod in the other.

"You *naughty* little ruffian," exploded his captor. "How *dare* you trespass in my grounds and steal my fruit?"

11 ***Monday***

12 ***Tuesday***

13 ***Wednesday***

14 ***Thursday***

15 ***Friday***

16 ***Saturday***

17 ***Sunday***

William had always felt bitter about what he considered the undue importance given to birds. People making a fuss of them and putting out nuts and things for them all over the place. You might starve for all they cared as long as *birds* had plenty of coconuts and stuff. Bird sanctuary indeed! Why not a boy sanctuary? A wood entirely devoted to boys—grown-ups not allowed to enter. Tables of chocolate cream and humbugs and lollypops at intervals. Boy baths of lemonade and orange squash. Cream buns hanging from trees. Instead of nesting-boxes, toys placed against all the trees—motor boats, bows and arrows, electric trains, cricket sets, footballs.

A boy sanctuary. He wondered no one had ever thought of it before. Fancy taking all this trouble all these years over bird sanctuaries and no one ever having thought of a boy sanctuary!

18 *Monday*

19 *Tuesday*

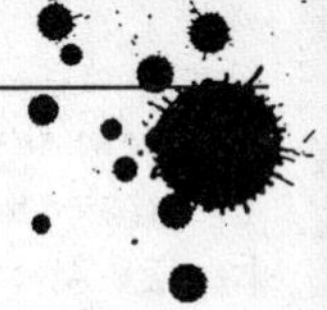

20 *Wednesday*

21 *Thursday*

22 *Friday*

23 *Saturday*

24 *Sunday*

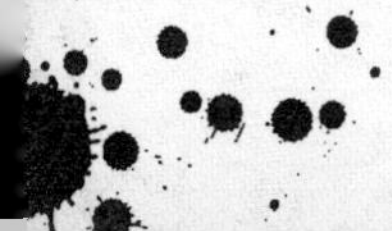

William says:

"I think that we all ought to take the greatest care of our brains in childhood because when we are grown up we may want to use them in some emergency and it would be very disappointing to find them all wore out—which I think is what often happens to grown ups. I try to take great care of mine by not usin' it too much."

25 ***Monday***

26 ***Tuesday***

27 *Wednesday*

28 *Thursday*

29 *Friday*

30 *Saturday*

1 *Sunday*

WILLIAM TAKES UP SCREEN WORK, AND FINDS IT A PAYING BUSINESS

from *The Happy Mag*, January 1931

William says:

"I think that every dentist ought to have to do a wild animal's teeth by lor, jus' to punish them for torcherin' people. I bet there wouldn't be many of em left after that, an' I jolly well wouldn't be sorry. I don't know why anyone ever started 'em at all. I bet that, when ordin'ry torcherin' in the Tower an' such like was stopped by lor, the torcherers set up as dentists, an' I bet all those little pickaxes an' things they use are what was left of the torcher instruments out of the torcher chambers."

2 ***Monday***

3 ***Tuesday***

4 ***Wednesday***

5 ***Thursday***

6 ***Friday***

7 ***Saturday***

8 ***Sunday***

William put the policeman's helmet on, stood on a chair and looked at himself in the mirror over the mantelpiece. The effect—or so it seemed to William—was magnificent, stupendous. He got down from the chair and swaggered about the room, seeing himself as a tall, majestic, ferocious-looking policeman of enormous girth and height. From this imaginary eminence he scowled threateningly down upon imaginary criminals, clapped handcuffs upon them, hustled them off to prison . . .

"*Would* you?" he said grimly through his teeth, as he tackled a gang of desperate dare-devils and by neat twists of ju-jitsu laid them all sprawling and helpless at his feet.

9 ***Monday***

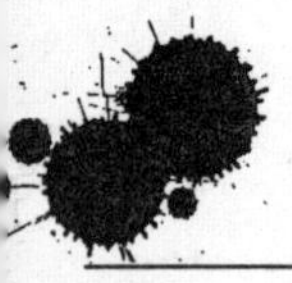

10 ***Tuesday***

11 ***Wednesday***

12 ***Thursday***

13 ***Friday***

14 ***Saturday***

15 ***Sunday***

"I want first to tell you the story of the play of which you are going to act a scene for the shield that I am presenting," Mr Welbecker said. "There was a man called Hamlet —"

"You just said he was called Bacon," said William.

"I did *not* say he was called Bacon," snapped Mr Welbecker.

"Yes, 'scuse me, you did," said William politely. "When I called him Ham you said it was Bacon, and now you're calling him Ham yourself."

"This was a different man," said Mr Welbecker. "*Listen!* This man was called Hamlet and his uncle had killed his father because he wanted to marry his mother."

"What did he want to marry his mother for?" said William. "I've never heard of anyone wanting to marry their mother."

"It was *Hamlet's* mother he wanted to marry."

"Oh, that man that you think wrote the plays."

"No, that was Bacon."

"You said it was Ham a minute ago. Whenever I say it's Bacon you say it's Ham, and whenever I say it's Ham you say it's Bacon. I don't think you know *which* his name was."

16 ***Monday***

17 ***Tuesday***

18 *Wednesday*

19 *Thursday*

20 *Friday*

21 *Saturday*

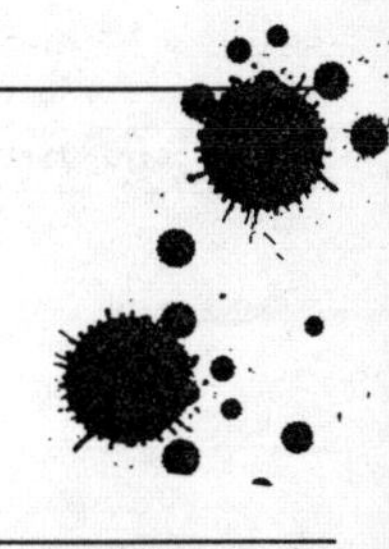

22 *Sunday*

William spent half an hour over a single sum, in which he came to the conclusion that it would take four men three hundred years to mow a meadow of two square acres.

23 *Monday*

24 *Tuesday*

25 ***Wednesday***

26 ***Thursday***

27 ***Friday***

28 ***Saturday***

29 ***Sunday***

William considered that the microbe world was treating him unfairly. Mild chicken-pox would be, on the whole, a welcome break in the monotony of life. It would mean delicacies such as jelly and cream and chicken. It would mean respite from the pressing claims of education.

It would afford an excuse for disinclination to work for months afterwards. William was an expert in the tired look and deep sigh that, for many months after an illness, would touch his mother's heart and make her tell him to put his books away and go out for a walk. No one could rival William in extracting the last ounce of profit from a slight indisposition.

30 *Monday*

31 *Tuesday*

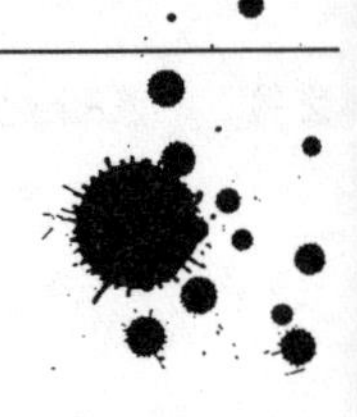

1 *Wednesday*

2 ***Thursday***

3 ***Friday***

4 ***Saturday***

5 ***Sunday***

Did you know?

Henry has an older brother called John and a young sister, but we are never told her name.

GUY FAWKES—WITH VARIATIONS

William, wearing Joan's coat and hat—the hat pulled well down over his eyes—came out of the old barn and addressed the guards outside in a high-pitched squeaky voice.

"Thank thee, varlets," he said, "for letting me visit my husband, Mr Guy Fawkes. I won't forget the bulls' eyes on Saturday. Good afternoon," and hurried away across the field down towards the road.

In order to make the situation more exciting, the guards had agreed to wait about five minutes before discovering the "trick" played on them. This would give William time to escape and afford an opportunity for a hunt over the countryside.

William had decided to make for the woods, where he knew of several good hiding-places. He had entered fully into his role and saw himself as Guy Fawkes, dressed in his wife's clothes, bent on eluding his pursuers. It was annoying to run straight into a tall woman walking down the road.

She gazed at him through horn-rimmed spectacles. Miss Cummins had noticed the old barn and had seen the figure in green coat and hat leave it to hurry across the field.

"It's Joan, isn't it?" she said tentatively.

"Uh-huh," said William, looking up at her.

Miss Cummins started. As head mistress of a large girls' school she was familiar with various degrees of plainness in her pupils, but she thought she had never come across such an uncompromisingly ugly little girl in all her life before. And not only ugly—but hard, brazen, tough. Yes, tough was the word. A tough little girl. Miss Cummins shuddered at the combination. Scowling aggressively, William returned her gaze.

"D'you want anything?" he said impolitely.

"Are you Joan Parfitt?" said Miss Cummins.

"Yeah," said William.

from *William Carries On*

William says:
"I've always wanted to turn on the bathroom taps and let them run till they'd made a waterfall down the stairs. It would make a fine waterfall, and I don't see that it could do any harm except just wet the stair carpet which would soon dry."

6 ***Monday***

7 ***Tuesday***

8 *Wednesday*

9 *Thursday*

10 *Friday*

11 *Saturday*

12 *Sunday*

"William," said Barbara pleasantly, "I can *dweam*. Can you?"

He made no answer.

"Answer your cousin, William," said his mother.

He swallowed, then spoke plaintively, "You always say not to talk with my mouth full," he said.

"You could speak when you've finished the mouthful."

"No. 'Cause I want to fill it again then," said William, firmly.

13 ***Monday***

14 ***Tuesday***

15 ***Wednesday***

16 ***Thursday***

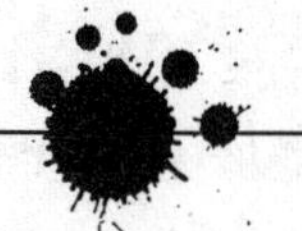

17 ***Friday***

18 ***Saturday***

19 ***Sunday***

William's Deadly Enemy

Hubert Lane made his first appearance in a story called "William—the Match-Maker" (*Still—William*). He is in forty-four stories, and is mentioned in another eleven.

OUR MANNYFESTO

Habby. Ass. Corpuss.
Magner Carter,

1. As much hollidays as term.
2. No afternoon School.
3. Sixpence a week pocket munny and not to be took off.
4. No Latin no French no Arithmetick.
5. As much ice creem and banarnas and creem buns as we like free.
6. No punnishments and stay up as late as we like.

20 *Monday*

21 *Tuesday*

NOVEMBER

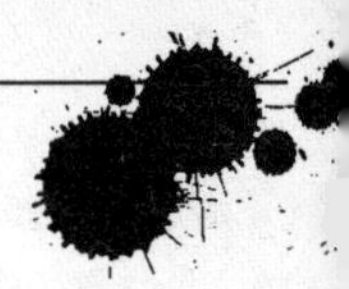

22 *Wednesday*

23 *Thursday*

24 *Friday*

25 *Saturday*

26 *Sunday*

William says:
"Parents' memories are the most extr'ordin'ry things. If it's anythin' you particular want them to remember, they forget it, an' if it's anythin' you particular want them to forget they remember it."

27 ***Monday***

28 ***Tuesday***

29 ***Wednesday***

30 ***Thursday***

1 ***Friday***

2 ***Saturday***

3 ***Sunday***

William says:

"I'm a jolly good boxer an' I've made a jolly good pair of boxin' gloves out of an old pair of gloves of father's, stuffin' 'em with paper. Las' time I had a boxin' match with Ginger, I made his nose bleed so's it went on bleedin' for nearly five minutes. Well, anyone'd pay to see that, wun't they? He made mine bleed, too, but it din't bleed as long as his."

4 ***Monday***

5 ***Tuesday***

6 ***Wednesday***

7 ***Thursday***

8 ***Friday***

9 ***Saturday***

10 ***Sunday***

"William," said Mrs Bruce Monkton-Bruce, weakly, "it was a gentle whistle we wanted to hear. A whistle like—like—like the wind in the distance. A *long* way in the distance, William."

William emitted a gentle, drawn-out, mournful whistle. It represented perfectly the distant moaning of the wind. His stricken audience recovered and gave a gasp of amazement and delight.

"That was *very* nice," said Mrs Bruce Monkton-Bruce.

William, cheered and flattered by her praise, said: "I'll do it a bit nearer than that now," and again gathered his forces for the effort.

"No, William," said Mrs Bruce Monkton-Bruce again stopping him just in time. "That's as near as we want."

11 *Monday*

12 *Tuesday*

13 Wednesday

14 Thursday

15 Friday

16 Saturday

17 Sunday

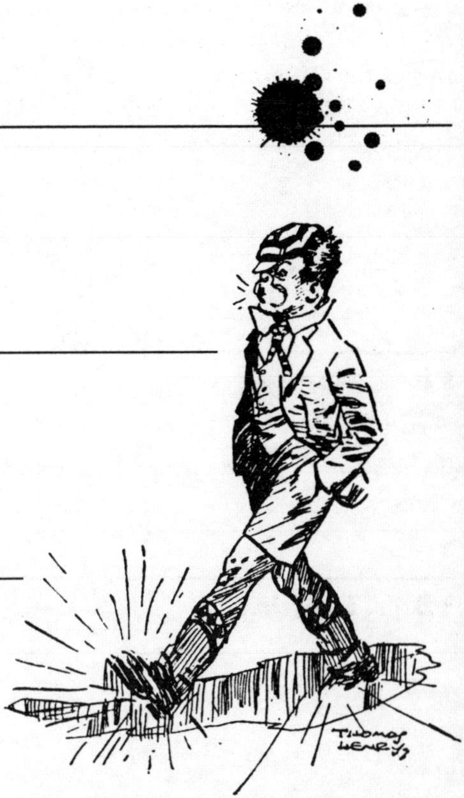

William says:
"If I was a king, I'd make a law that no one was to mention money boxes or savin' on Christmas Day, and anyone what mentioned a money box or savin' was to be put in prison for a year."

18 ***Monday***

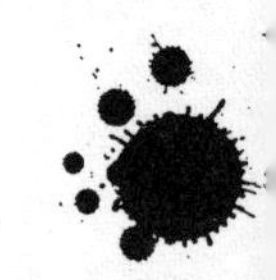

19 ***Tuesday***

20 ***Wednesday***

21 ***Thursday***

22 ***Friday***

23 ***Saturday***

24 ***Sunday***

WILLIAM'S CHRISTMAS EVE

It was Christmas. The air was full of excitement and secrecy. William, whose old-time faith in notes to Father Christmas sent up the chimney had died a natural death as the result of bitter experience, had thoughtfully presented each of his friends and relations with a list of his immediate requirements.

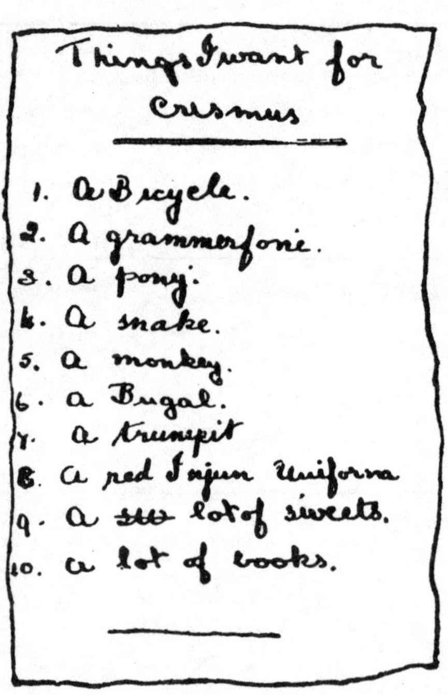

Things I want for Crismus

1. a Bicycle.
2. a grammerfone.
3. a pony.
4. a snake.
5. a monkey.
6. a Bugal.
7. a trumpit
8. a red Injun Uniform
9. a lot of sweets.
10. a lot of books.

He had a vague and not unfounded misgiving that his family would begin at the bottom of the list instead of the top. He was not surprised, therefore, when he saw his father come home rather later than usual carrying a parcel of books under his arm. A few days afterwards he announced casually at breakfast:

"Well, I only hope no one gives me *The Great Chief*, or *The Pirate Ship*, or *The Land of Danger* for Christmas."

His father started.

"Why?" he said sharply.

"Jus' 'cause I've read them, that's all," explained William with a bland look of innocence.

The glance that Mr Brown threw at his offspring was not altogether devoid of suspicion, but he said nothing. He set off after breakfast with the same parcel of books under his arm and returned with another. This time, however, he did not put them in the library cupboard, and William searched in vain.

from *More William*

WILLIAM'S
XMAS EVE
BORROWED GINGERS GRAMAFONE AN ROBERTS WIG
MADE NINEPENCE TOWARDS A PIRATE OUTFIT
NO-EL NO-EL
TRIED TO MAKE THINGS LOOK A BIT MORE LIKE CHRISMAS
FLOUR
FLOUR
CR-R-R-R
OBLIJED AUNT BETTY. SHE SAID IT WASNT CHRISMAS WITHOUT A GHOST
HERD SCREAMS AND LANGWIDGE FROM ROBERT'S ROOM
OF COURSE THE FAMILY WOULD S'PECT ME BUT WHEN THEY RUSHED INTO MY ROOM WAS FAST ASLEEP

from *The Happy Mag*, January 1936

Extracts from William's Christmas Day Diary
10.30 Go to church. Sermon about being kind to people. Look at my family and hope they're taking it in, but none of them seem to be listening.

2.45 Play with Plasticine.
Cover hair with it to see what I'd look like bald. Find I'd look jolly funny. Try to take it off, but it won't come.

25 ***Monday***

26 ***Tuesday***

27 *Wednesday*

28 *Thursday*

29 *Friday*

30 *Saturday*

31 *Sunday*

WILLIAM'S TRUTHFUL CHRISTMAS

Lady Atkinson was stout and elderly and wore a very youthful hat and coat.

"A happy Christmas to you all!" she said graciously. "The boy? Your nephew? William? How do you do, William? He—*stares* rather, doesn't he? Ah, yes," she greeted every one separately with infinite condescension.

"I've brought you my Christmas presents in person," she went on in the tone of voice of one giving an unheard-of treat. "Look!"

She took out of an envelope a large signed photograph of herself. "There now . . . what do you think of that?"

Murmurs of surprise and admiration and gratitude.

Lady Atkinson drank them in complacently.

"It's very good isn't it? You . . . little boy . . . don't you think it's very like me?"

William gazed at it critically.

"It's not as fat as you are," was his final offering at the altar of truth.

"*William!*" screamed Mrs Brown, "how *can* you be so impolite!"

"Impolite?" said William with some indignation. "I'm not tryin' to be polite! I'm bein' truthful. I can't be everything. Seems to me I'm the only person in the world what *is* truthful an' no one seems to be grateful to me. It *isn't*'s fat as what she is," he went on doggedly, "an' it's not got as many little lines on its face as what she has an' it's different lookin' altogether. It looks pretty an' she doesn't——"

Lady Atkinson towered over him, quivering with rage.

"You *nasty* little boy!" she said thrusting her face close to his. "You—NASTY—little—boy!"

Then she swept out of the room without another word.

The front door slammed.

She was gone.

Aunt Emma sat down and began to weep.

"She'll never come to the house again," she said.

"I always said he ought to be hung," said Robert gloomily. "Every day we let him live he complicates our lives still worse."

"I shall tell your father, William," said Mrs Brown, "*directly* we get home."

"The kindest thing to think," said Ethel, "is that he's mad."

"Well," said William, "I don' know what I've done 'cept cast aside deceit an'—an' the other thing what he said in church an' speak the truth an' that. I don' know why every one's so mad at me jus' 'cause of that. You'd think they'd be glad!"

from *Still—William*

SOURCES OF QUOTATIONS

Dec 26 New Year's Day (*Happy Mag*, Jan 1927). **Jan 2** The Mystery of Oaklands (*William*). **Jan 9** William and the Begging Letter (*William and A.R.P.*). **Jan 16** A Crowded Hour with William (*William's Crowded Hours*). **Jan 23** William Writes a Play (*Happy Mag*, Xmas 1929). **Jan 30** The Plan that Failed (*William — The Outlaw*). **Feb 6** William Goes Shopping (*William's Happy Days*). **Feb 13** A Rescue Party (*William—The Rebel*). **Feb 20** William the Invisible (*William—The Detective*). **Feb 27** William Goes to the Pictures (*Just—William*). **Mar 6** (*Just William's Luck*). **Mar 13** When is a Treat Not a Treat? (*Happy Mag*, Xmas 1928). **Mar 20** William Meets the Professor (*William and the Tramp*). **Mar 27** The Outlaws and the Hidden Treasure (*William's Happy Days*). **Apr 3** The Job I'd Like Best (*Happy Mag*, Dec 1927). **Apr 10** William the Money-Maker (*William — The Good*). **Apr 17** William Joins the Waits (*William In Trouble*). **Apr 24** Let's Go Back to Caves (*Tit-Bits Summer Annual*, 1932). **May 1** William and the Black-Out (*William and the Evacuees*). **May 8** The Plan that Failed (*William's Crowded Hours*). **May 15** Don William and the Sun-Bather (*William — The Explorer*). **May 22** Picnics (*Tit-Bits Summer Annual*, 1929). **May 29** Brighter and Better Pets (*Happy Mag*, Xmas 1930). **Jun 5** Only Just in Time (*William—The Gangster*). **Jun 12** William and the Black Cat (*William — The Fourth*). **Jun 19** William's Midsummer Eve (*William Carries On*). **Jun 26** William's Birthday (*William's Happy Days*). **Jul 3** My Day in London (*Tit-Bits Summer Annual*, 1928). **Jul 10** William and the Over-Ten Club (*William and the Moon Rocket*). **Jul 17** All the News (*William—In Trouble*). **Jul 24** My Day in London (*Tit-Bits Summer Annual*, 1928). **Jul 31** Something Like a Change (*Happy Mag*, Sep 1927). **Aug 7** William Catches His Trains (*William the Lawless*). **Aug 14** How I Would Improve the Seaside (*Tit-Bits Summer Annual*, 1931?). **Aug 21** A Witch in Time (*William—The Bold*). **Aug 28** William and the Early Romans (*William—In Trouble*). **Sep 4** School Is a Waste of Time! (*Happy Mag*, Sep 1927). **Sep 11** William's Double Life (*William*). **Sep 18** William the Globe-Trotter (*William — The Showman*). **Sep 25** Commonsense About Holidays (*Tit-Bits Summer Annual*, 1927). **Oct 2** William and the Dentist (*William — The Dictator*). **Oct 9** William and the Policeman's Helmet (*Sweet William*). **Oct 16** William Holds the Stage (*William—The Pirate*). **Oct 23** William and the Wonderful Present (*Sweet William*). **Oct 30** William's Secret Society (*William Again*). **Nov 6** New Rules for December 25th (*Happy Mag*, Jan 1932). **Nov 13** A Busy Day (*More William*). **Nov 20** The Outlaws' Report (*William and the Brains Trust*). **Nov 27** I'll Tell You What's Wrong With Christmas (*Happy Mag*, Xmas 1930). **Dec 4** William Helps the Cause (*William's Happy Days*). **Dec 11** William — the Great Actor (*William—The Good*). **Dec 18** I'll Tell You What's Wrong With Christmas (*Happy Mag*, Xmas 1930). **Dec 25** Christmas Day with William (*Happy Mag*, Xmas 1932).